Read Write Inc.

Literacy and Language
Anthology 2 Book 2

Janey Pursglove and **Charlotte Raby**

Series developed by **Ruth Miskin**

Contents

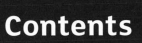

OXFORD
UNIVERSITY PRESS

Oh, Gnome!

Lou Kuenzler

Characters

Oliver
an 8-year-old boy

Katie
his twin sister

Jerome
a garden gnome

Gran
a keen gardener

Scene 1

Katie is amongst the neat flower beds in her grandparents' garden. Oliver runs towards her.

Oliver   *(Waving a cricket bat **triumphantly**)* Look what I found! It was in the back of the garage. And there's a proper hard cricket ball too.

Katie   Brilliant! I'll bat, you bowl.

Jerome *(In a fishing position, on top of a painted toadstool. He talks directly to the audience. The children cannot hear him.)* Yikes! I don't like the sound of this! Two children, plus one bat, plus one ball, equals disaster!

(Katie takes the bat and practises swinging it. Oliver tosses the ball in the air and catches it.)

Katie *(Skidding down the garden, ready to bat)* We need to be careful, though.

Jerome She's right about that! If they had any brains in their big, squishy heads, they wouldn't play at all!

Katie You know how proud Grandma is of her garden. We better not break anything.

Oliver What is there to break?

Jerome Er…me! The little guy with a fishing rod! I'm only made of clay, you know! *(The children, of course, cannot hear him.)*

Oliver   If we keep off the flower beds and away from the greenhouse, nothing else can come to any harm. Can it?

Katie   What about that cute little gnome?

Jerome   I'm beginning to like this one!

(The twins peer down at Jerome.)

Oliver   He's not cute! Look at his face! He looks like an angry potato!

Katie   *(Giggling)* He does look a bit grumpy!

(They both laugh.)

Jerome   Charming! First you find a **lethal** weapon, then you insult me.

Gran   *(Calling from the doorway)* Is that Grandpa's old cricket bat? Wherever did you dig that up? *(She raises her hands in horror)* And a proper hard ball, too! You can't play with that in the garden!

Oliver But we love cricket!

Gran Imagine if you hit something **fragile** – like my little gnome. He's my pride and joy! He's got such character. Every time I look at his little face I want to smile!

Jerome At last! Someone **appreciates** me! I came brand new from a garden centre, you know…not some old piece of junk that was picked up at a car boot sale.

Katie We'll be really careful…

Gran Wait until after lunch. We'll go to the shops and buy a soft ball to use. There's pizza in the oven. It'll only take a few minutes. *(She goes back into the house.)*

Oliver *(Whispering)* Just let me bowl once, Katie. There's a spin shot I really want to try.

Katie and Jerome *(Together)* Grandma said no!

The Mime

The following sequence should be presented in slow motion, with the cricket bat and ball mimed. There should be no sound or words, although the actors' faces can show their expressions…

As Jerome and Katie speak their last line, Oliver is already bowling. Katie is caught off guard and hits the ball wildly. The children turn their heads and watch, horrified, as the shot heads towards Jerome. (End mime)

Everyone gasps.

THWACK! *The shot hits Jerome and he falls to the floor.*

Katie   Now look what you've done! You knocked him right off his toadstool!

Oliver   You were batting!

Jerome   *(Weakly, but still holding his fishing rod)* Can somebody call a gnome ambulance?

Katie   *(Crouching)* What will we tell Grandma?

Oliver   Nothing! Just try to put him back up.

Katie   It'll never work. He's snapped right off at the base.

Oliver   We could pretend next door's cat did it…?

Katie   Or the wind…?

Oliver   If we don't say anything, perhaps Gran won't even notice.

Katie   But she said he was her pride and joy…

Gran   *(Calling)* Pizza's ready!

Jerome   Ha! Now there'll be trouble! *(Directly to the audience)*
             I wouldn't like to be in their shoes, would you?

Gran   What are you two up to?

Katie and Oliver   *(Together)* Nothing!

Katie   *(Whispering)* We'll have to tell her.

Oliver   *(Under his breath)* But she'll be furious!
              I bet we won't even get our pizza!

Katie   Perhaps. But it'll be better in the end if we tell the truth.

Oliver   It is the right thing…
              We'll just have to own up.

Katie   Grandma…

Oliver   We've done something really silly.

             (They step away from the gnome and Gran gasps.)

Scene 2

Jerome has been glued back on to his toadstool. The twins are standing beside Gran, still looking thoroughly ashamed.

Katie   We're truly sorry.

Oliver   I should never have bowled. Especially when you told us we shouldn't.

Gran   (*Gently*) At least you understand how silly you were.

Oliver   Gran, why aren't you more cross with us?

Gran   I suppose I'm pleased, in a funny way.

Jerome   Pleased! They tried to break me into a million pieces!

Katie   I don't understand…

Gran   I *was* cross because you disobeyed me. But I'm pleased you told me the truth. Seeing you own up and be honest is worth much more than a silly old garden gnome!

Jerome   Hold on! I thought I was your treasured possession. Next thing you'll be packing me off to a car boot sale! Or swapping me for a bird table!

Gran   Imagine how disappointed I would have been if you'd tried to blame it on next door's cat.

Katie   *(Looking at her shoes)* Or the wind…

Gran   I'm proud that you told me the truth! I wasn't nearly as cross as I would have been if you had tried to trick me or tell lies.

Oliver   And I'm glad the gnome is fixed.

Jerome   Easy for you to say! You weren't the one who had super-strong glue poured on his… Well, poured on the place where he sits down.

Oliver   But it *was* the most brilliant spin shot, Gran. You should have seen it!

Gran   *(Raises her eyebrows)* Let's have that pizza, before it's stone cold.

Jerome   Don't worry about me…

(As they exit, we hear Jerome mumbling in disgust.)

Jerome   Nobody appreciates me… Why do I sit here, day after day, pretending to fish? There isn't even a pond…

Denton Community Group asks you to:

Think **big**...
Think **bigger**...
Now think **massive**...

The Super Car Boot

TOY SALE!

If **classic dolls** and **action figures** are what you're after, all your dreams are about to come true!

Pick up your favourite **games consoles** at rock-bottom prices – they'll all be here.

Plus!
Tea, coffee, cold drinks and **cakes, cakes, cakes**

Sellers: gates open 6.30 a.m. Set up your stall for just £8.
Buyers: gates open 8.00 a.m. Entry £1 per person (kids under 5 free!)

Gnome, **Sweet** Gnome!

Gnome more waiting!

The Denton Gnome Centre is here!

The Denton Gnome Centre, *Number One for Gnomes*, make gnome mistake!

Gnome matter what you need, we've got it!

As well as fishing gnomes, we have:

- planting gnomes
- grass-mowing gnomes
- wheelbarrow gnomes.

Don't leave your gnome alone!

Come to our grand opening and pick up one of our special first day offers:

- Buy **two** full-size gnomes and get a **third** absolutely **FREE**!
- Buy a **six**-gnome family set and pay for only **four**!

Why not make a day of it? Have lunch in our 5-star café, or bring your own snacks and sun yourself in our grassy picnic area.

For more information, call us on 05432 123456, or visit our website at www.dentongnomes.con

Beauty and the Beast

Gill Howell

Once upon a time, there was a merchant who had three daughters. He loved all three but kept a special place in his heart for Beauty, the youngest daughter. Beauty was always sweet-natured and cheerful, unlike the other daughters, who were often grumpy and jealous.

A day came when the merchant had to go away on important business. As he would be gone for some time, he said to his daughters, "What gifts would you like me to bring you?"

The eldest asked for jewels. The second asked for fine clothes.

Beauty said, "Dear father, there is nothing I need. Just your safe return." Her father insisted, so she replied at last, "Then bring me the loveliest rose you can find."

The merchant's business went well and finally he began his long journey home. In his bag were the gifts for his daughters…apart from Beauty's rose.

'I will find one on my journey,' he thought. Instantly, a great storm broke out across the sky.

Through the lashing rain, the merchant saw a gleam of light. Hoping to find shelter, he galloped towards it and discovered that it came from a **magnificent** castle surrounded by beautiful gardens.

The merchant approached the great front door. It swung open. **Cautiously**, he entered the hallway. "Hello!" he cried. "Is anyone here?"

There was light shining into the hall from a doorway, so, thinking the owner might be there, the merchant entered the room. He saw a table laid for supper. A letter lay beside a single plate. It simply read:

Please accept my hospitality.

The merchant enjoyed a delicious meal, then waited for the mysterious host. **Lulled** by the warmth of the crackling log fire, he found himself drifting into a deep sleep…

The next morning, the storm had passed, but still no host came. The merchant prepared to leave. Then he caught sight of the garden.

There, in the centre, was the loveliest rose ever: one strong stem with a single crimson flower.

"Beauty's rose!" he exclaimed.

The merchant hurried out into the garden and plucked it. As he put his nose to the sweet-smelling petals, an angry roar split the silence.

"Is this how you repay my kindness?" A hideous beast came charging towards the merchant. "You will pay for that rose with your life!" he cried.

"Sire," the merchant pleaded, "I only wanted a rose for my daughter. If you saw her, you would know why she deserves the loveliest of all roses!"

The merchant told the Beast about Beauty. The Beast listened and agreed to let the merchant go home to give Beauty the rose, on one condition. "You must return and live here with me."

With a heavy heart, the merchant was forced to agree to the Beast's demand.

Full of sorrow, he returned home and explained the promise he had made to the Beast.

Beauty couldn't stand the thought of her father being unhappy. One night, without telling anyone, she left and travelled to the Beast's castle, determined to take her father's place.

At first she was afraid, but the Beast stayed hidden and left many gifts and kind notes for her. Beauty grew fond of him, though he was puzzling, and she would talk to him whenever she sensed he was near.

One day, she finally caught a glimpse of him. Though she trembled inside, Beauty showed no fear at his ugly, hair-covered face or the fangs that stuck out of his mouth, so the Beast began to sit and talk with her each day.

Despite the Beast's kindness, Beauty was lonely. "If only I could see my dear father once more," she said, sighing.

The Beast could not bear to see her unhappy, so he gave her a wonderful magic mirror in which she could see the people she loved. Beauty felt comforted at first, but then grew frightened as she saw that her father's guilt was making him ill. As winter approached, there came a terrible day when she feared he was dying.

At once, she found the Beast and begged to go home. "I must see him, before it's too late!" she pleaded.

The Beast agreed, but on one condition. Beauty must promise to return within one week. Beauty promised, then left for home as quickly as she could.

The merchant was so happy to see Beauty that he soon recovered. Beauty's sisters, however, tricked her into staying too long. One day, she looked into her magic mirror. To her horror, she saw the Beast lying as if dead near the rose bush.

"Oh, I have broken my promise and broken the poor Beast's heart!" she cried, fearfully.

Beauty rushed to the castle to find the Beast. He lay unmoving beside Beauty's rose, with leaves and petals tumbling around him in the cold air.

"Oh, Beast, dearest Beast, don't die!" cried Beauty. "Your ugliness will *never* stop me loving you. I will *never* leave you again… I want to be your wife!"

Beauty knelt to kiss the Beast. As she did so, he was transformed in front of her eyes! His hairy face and fangs magically vanished and a handsome prince stood there in his place.

"What have you done with my dear Beast?" Beauty gasped.

The Prince explained. "An evil fairy cast a spell on me. I would remain an ugly beast until a beautiful girl asked to marry me. Your words have broken the spell!"

So Beauty married the handsome Prince. Her father and sisters came to live in the castle with them and they all lived happily ever after.

How to Turn a Class Hamster into a Dinosaur

First, prepare your hamster
for life as a ferocious, school-eating dinosaur.
Show it pictures of what life was like
when dinosaurs roamed the earth.
(Ask a teacher.)

Next, motivate it.
Give it lessons on how to scare teachers.
(Diagrams may help.)
Get some prehistoric gooey stuff,
from places unexplored in millions of years...
(if your brother has his own room,
it is always a good idea to start looking there).

Smear this gunk on the walls
of the school you want chomped
whilst chanting:
Teachers run and scream and stumble
make a tasty red brick crumble!
Make a giant dino gangsta!
Megasaurus Biggus Hampsta!
Repeat until satisfied.
You now have your very own
Turbosaurus Hamster-beast.

Feed Carefully.

Matt Lees